Little Bulld

Story by Beverley Randell
Illustrated by Marina McAllan

2

This is Little Bulldozer.

4

Little Bulldozer went to look
at a fire engine.

"Hello, Fire Engine,"
said Little Bulldozer.
"I like helping.
I will help you."

"Go away. Go away,"
said the fire engine.
"I'm going to a fire.
You are too little
to help at a fire.
Go away."

Little Bulldozer
went away.
He went to look
at a big truck.
"Hello, Big Truck,"
he said.
"I like helping.
I will help you."

9

"Go away, Little Bulldozer,"
said the big truck.
"You are too little to help me.
Go away and play."

Little Bulldozer went away.
He cried and cried.
"I'm too little," he said.

"Hello, Little Bulldozer,"
said a big bulldozer.
"Come and help me with this tree."

"I'm too little to help you,"
said Little Bulldozer.

"Come on. You are not too little,"
said the big bulldozer.

Little Bulldozer went to help.
He helped and helped.

"Thank you," said the big bulldozer.

"I'm not too little, am I?"
said Little Bulldozer.
"I'm **not** too little
to help."